⊲ P9-DIZ-106

How do I use this scheme?

Key Words with Peter and Jane has three
parallel series, each containing twelve books. All three
series are written using the same carefully controlled
vocabulary. Readers will get the most out of **Key Words** with
Peter and Jane when they follow the books in the pattern
1a, 1b, 1c; 2a, 2b, 2c and so on.

• Series a
gradually introduces and repeats new words.

• Series b
provides further practice of these same words, but
in a different context and with different illustrations.

• Series c
uses familiar words to teach **phonics** in a methodical way,
enabling children to read increasingly difficult words.
It also provides a link to writing.

Published by Ladybird Books Ltd
A Penguin Company
Penguin Books Ltd., 80 Strand, London WC2R 0RL, UK
Penguin Books Australia Ltd., Camberwell, Victoria, Australia
Penguin Group (NZ) 67 Apollo Drive, Rosedale, North Shore 0632, New Zealand

007 - 10 9 8 7

© LADYBIRD BOOKS LTD MCMLXIV, this edition MMIX

LADYBIRD and the device of a ladybird are trademarks of Ladybird Books Ltd.
All rights reserved. No part of this publication may be reproduced,
stored in a retrieval system, or transmitted in any form or by any means,
electronic, mechanical, photocopying, recording or otherwise,
without the prior consent of the copyright owner.

ISBN: 978-1-40930-146-2

Printed in China

Key Words

with Peter and Jane

9c Enjoying reading

written by W. Murray
illustrated by M. Aitchison

Sounds we know from Book 8c.

1 **ai** as in ch**ai**n.

2 **ay** as in h**ay**.

3 **oa** as in b**oa**t.

4 **st** as in **st**amp.

5 **nd** as in po**nd**.

6 **ow** as in c**ow**.

7 **aw** as in s**aw**.

8 **ce** as in mi**ce**.

9 **ck** as in ro**ck**.

10 **ar** as in c**ar**.

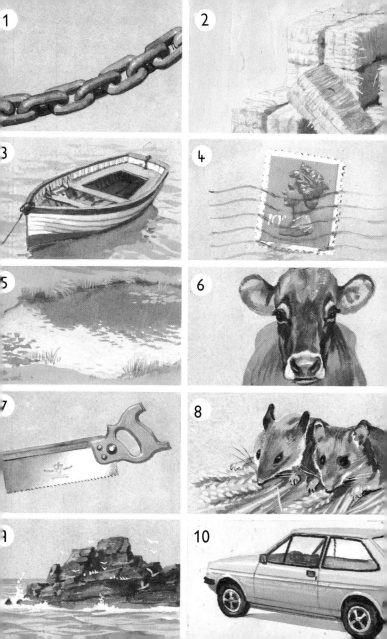

sp

We know the words: **sports** and **hospital**.

We can learn: **spin, spell, spill, spoon, spade, spend, spot, wasp.**

1   The boy wants to spin his top.

2   The girl learns to spell.

3   She spills some milk.

4   He uses a spoon.

5   The boy works with a spade.

6   They have money to spend.

7   He says, "X marks the spot."

8   A wasp is by the jam.

spell
spin
spill
spoon

-y

We know the words: **many, happy, baby, lovely, lorry, puppy** and **sunny.**

We can learn: **jelly, funny, windy, holly, lady, daisy.**

1   Here is a jelly.

2   The clown is funny.

3   The man is in a lorry.

4   The day is windy.

5   She picks some holly.

6   Here is a lady.

7   The baby has a daisy.

8   The puppy is happy.

-ed

We know the word: **picked.**

We can learn: **cooked, locked, stopped, climbed, kicked, dressed, closed, pushed.**

1 The ham has been cooked.

2 The door is locked.

3 The policeman has stopped the car.

4 The boy has climbed the tree.

5 The man has kicked the ball.

6 She is dressed like a queen.

7 He has closed the door.

8 The horse has pushed open the gate.

2

3

4

5

6

7

8

tr

We know the words: **tree** and **train.**

We can learn: **trap, trench, trick, trunk, track, tramp, trips, trot.**

1   This is a trap.

2   The man makes a trench.

3   He does a card trick.

4   The boy looks in a trunk.

5   Here is a track through the woods.

6   This is a tramp.

7   The boy trips and falls.

8   She makes the donkey trot.

Complete the words as you write them in your exercise book. The pictures will help you.

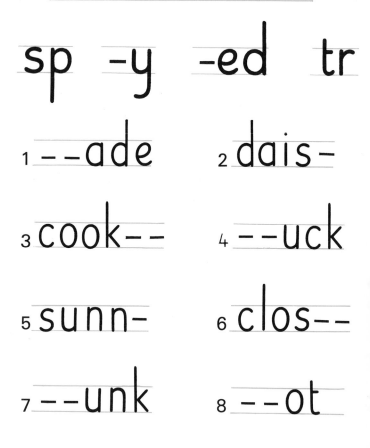

sp   -y   -ed   tr

1 --ade   2 dais-

3 cook--   4 --uck

5 sunn-   6 clos--

7 --unk   8 --ot

The answers are on Page 48.

cr

We know the words: **ice-cream** and **cricket.**

We can learn: **crab, crack, crash, cross, creeps, crust, crown, crush.**

1   Here is a crab.

2   There is a crack in the cup.

3   There has been a car crash.

4   A cross is on the hill.

5   The Indian creeps along.

6   He eats a crust.

7   The queen has a crown.

8   The apples are crushed.

1

2

3

4

5

6

8

–le

We know the words: **apple, little, uncle, whistle, kettle** and **table.**

We can learn: **middle, puddle, bundle, paddle, saddle, candle, rattle, handle.**

1   The boy is in the middle.

2   He walks in a puddle.

3   The tramp has a bundle.

4   The girl likes to paddle.

5   The donkey has a saddle.

6   She has a candle.

7   The baby holds a rattle.

8   This is a door handle.

‒mp

We know the words: **jump, camp** and **stamp.**

We can learn: **lamp, damp, ramp, bump, pump, stump, limp, empty.**

1 He has a lamp.

2 The towel is damp.

3 The car goes up the ramp.

4 He falls with a bump.

5 The boy works the pump.

6 They play by the tree stump.

7 The flowers are limp.

8 The jar is empty.

2

4

6

8

-oy

We know the words: **boy** and **toy.**

We can learn: **Roy** and **enjoy.**

1   Here is a boy at play.

2   The boy's name is Roy.

3   Roy has a new toy.

4   The boy is going to enjoy an ice-cream.

oi

We can also learn: **oil, boil, points, coin.**

5   The boy uses an oil can.

6   She sees the kettle boil.

7   The boy points the way.

8   The man spins the coin.

2

4

6

8

Complete the words as you write
them in your exercise book. The
pictures will help you.

cr -le -mp -oy oi

1 --ow

2 catt--

3 ca--

4 j--nt

5 bott--

6 --own

7 t--

8 ju--

The answers are on Page 48.

2

4

6

8

ir

We know the words: **bird, fir** and **first.**

We can learn: **dirt, Sir, shirt, birthday.**

1 She writes, Dear Sir . . . .
2 The boy falls in the dirt.
3 He puts on a shirt.
4 It is her birthday.

ur

We know the word: **hurt.**

We can learn: **burn, burst, fur, church.**

5 The wood will burn.
6 The balloon will burst.
7 The cat's fur is black.
8 Here is a church.

1

2

3

4

5

6

7

8

-nk

We know the words: **ink, drink, think, thank** and **trunk.**

We can learn: **pink, sink, rink, wink, bank, bunk, tank, ankle.**

1   Her dress is pink.

2   She is at the sink.

3   The boy is at an ice rink.

4   He gives a wink.

5   This is a bank.

6   The boy is in a bunk.

7   Here is a water tank.

8   He has hurt his ankle.

br

We know the words: **bring, brother** and **brush.**

We can learn: **brown, broom, brook, brick, branch, brim, bride, bridle.**

1   The horse is brown.

2   The man uses a broom.

3   The boy jumps the brook.

4   He picks up a brick.

5   The cat is on a branch.

6   The water is up to the brim.

7   Here comes the bride.

8   He puts a bridle on the horse.

or

We know the word: **horse.**

We can learn: **fork, cork, stork, fort, north, torch, short, cord.**

1 She picks up a fork.

2 He takes out the cork.

3 This is a stork.

4 The boy plays with a fort.

5 N is for North.

6 The girl holds a torch.

7 This boy is short.

8 He pulls on the cord.

Complete the words as you write
them in your exercise book. The
pictures will help you.

ir   ur   -nk   br   or

1 th--ty   2 n--se

3 tru--   4 --oom

5 st--k   6 f--k

7 --ick   8 i--

The answers are on Page 48.

1

2

3

4

5

6

7

8

It is the Christmas holiday for the boys. They are at play in the park. There is ice on the pond there. The boys think the ice is thick, but it is thin. One boy is in the middle of the ice when he trips and falls. There is a crack and the boy falls through the ice.

The boys call the park keeper to help their friend. He finds that he can reach the boy and he pulls him out of the water. The boy is not hurt, but he is very wet, so the park keeper takes him home.

Copy out and complete —

1 The b - - s play in the park.
2 They thi - - the ice is thick.
3 There is a - -ack as the boy falls.
4 His friends go f - - help.
5 They - -ing the park keeper to the pond.
6 The boy is wet but not h - - t.

The answers are on Page 49.

Two boys have come down the hill in their Go-Karts and have crashed one into the other. The boys fall out of the Go-Karts into the dirt. They are both dirty. One of the boys is not hurt but the other has hurt his ankle. He limps as he walks. The boy who is not hurt tells the other that he ought to go to the hospital to let the doctor or the nurse see his ankle.

They both go to the hospital. The nurse tells the boy that he will soon be well again.

Copy out and complete —

1   The Go-Karts have crash--
2   The boys fall into the d--t.
3   They are both dirt-.
4   One has hurt his ank--.
5   The boy li--s as he walks.
6   They go to the ho--ital.

The answers are on Page 49.

The girl comes out of the house into the garden to pick some apples. She wants to give some to a friend. There is a wasp on an apple but the girl does not see it. She puts her hand on the apple and the wasp stings her. The sting hurts the girl. She calls out and runs into the house to her mother.

The girl tells her mother about the wasp and points to the sting on her hand. Her mother puts something on it. Soon it does not hurt. Then she helps her to pick some apples for her friend.

Copy out and complete —

1 A wa-- is on an apple.
2 The wasp h--ts the girl.
3 She p--nts to the sting.
4 Mother looks at the st---.
5 They pi-- some apples.
6 The apples are f-- her friend.

The answers are on Page 49.

It has been raining all day and now there is a storm. The sky gets dark and it is very windy. The trees bend in the wind. A horse is by the trees. The man thinks the horse is in danger from the storm. He takes it to a stable. There he rubs the horse down and puts a rug over it.

As the man comes out of the stable he sees a tree crash down. The wind is blowing very hard now. The man runs quickly to his house which is not far away.

Copy out and complete —

1 It is very wind-.
2 There is a --orm.
3 The ---es bend in the wind.
4 A h--se is by the trees.
5 He thi--s the horse is in danger.
6 He sees a tree --ash down.

The answers are on Page 50.

The boy and girl work on a model of their home town. They enjoy themselves as they make the little houses, shops and other buildings. They use anything they can find for their work. The boy has made a little church out of card and a piece of candle. Two small pins make a cross. Now he makes some fir trees with straws and cloth.

His sister uses some matchboxes and some card to make a model hospital and then she paints the park green. She has a brush and some coloured inks. "This green ink is just the colour of grass," she says.

Copy out and complete —

1   The boy and girl enj-- themselves.
2   They make litt-- houses and shops.
3   Two small pins make a --oss.
4   He makes some f-- trees.
5   The girl has a --ush.
6   She uses colour-- inks.

The answers are on Page 50.

A man is up a tall tree. He cuts off the top of the tree and then saws off each branch. They crash down as he cuts them off.

Then he comes down and saws through the thick trunk of the tree. It cracks and then falls with a crash. Only the stump of the tree is left. Other men help him to cut the trunk into logs.

The men push and kick the logs into the water.

There is a hut by the trees where the men eat. They can sleep there, as there are bunks in the hut.

Copy out and complete —

1 The man cuts off each - -anch.
2 The branches - -ash down.
3 The man s- -s through the trunk.
4 Only the stu- - is left.
5 The men saw up the - -ee - -unk.
6 They pu- - the logs into the water.

The answers are on Page 50.

Pages 48 to 50 give the answers to the written exercises in this book.

Page 14

1	spade	2	daisy
3	cooked	4	truck
5	sunny	6	closed
7	trunk	8	spot

Page 24

1	crow	2	cattle
3	camp	4	joint
5	bottle	6	crown
7	toy	8	jump

Page 34

1	thirty	2	nurse
3	trunk	4	broom
5	stork	6	fork
7	brick	8	ink

Page 36

1 The boys play in the park.

2 They think the ice is thick.

3 There is a crack as the boy falls.

4 His friends go for help.

5 They bring the park keeper to the pond.

6 The boy is wet but not hurt.

Page 38

1 The Go-Karts have crashed.

2 The boys fall into the dirt.

3 They are both dirty.

4 One has hurt his ankle.

5 The boy limps as he walks.

6 They go to the hospital.

Page 40

1 A wasp is on an apple.

2 The wasp hurts the girl.

3 She points to the sting.

4 Mother looks at the sting.

5 They pick some apples.

6 The apples are for her friend.

Page 42

1　It is very windy.

2　There is a storm.

3　The trees bend in the wind.

4　A horse is by the trees.

5　He thinks the horse is in danger.

6　He sees a tree crash down.

Page 44

1　The boy and girl enjoy themselves.

2　They make little houses and shops.

3　Two small pins make a cross.

4　He makes some fir trees.

5　The girl has a brush.

6　She uses coloured inks.

Page 46

1　The man cuts off each branch.

2　The branches crash down.

3　The man saws through the trunk.

4　Only the stump is left.

5　The men saw up the tree trunk.

6　They push the logs into the water.

Book 4c

b	c	t	a
f	h	m	s

Book 5c

i	e	o	u
d	g	l	n

Book 6c

p	r	w	j	k	v
	x	y	z	qu	

Book 7c

ee	oo	ing	sh
ea	ch	er	ll
-e	th	wh	

Book 8c

ai	ay	oa	st
nd	ow	aw	-ce
	ck	ar	

Book 9c

sp	-y	ed	tr	cr
-le	-mp	oy	oi	ir
	ur	-nk	br	or

Learning by sounds

If children learn the sounds of letters and how to blend them with the other letter sounds (eg. c-a-t) they can tackle new words independently (eg. P-a-t).

In the initial stages it is best if these phonic words are already known to the learner.

However, not all English words can be learned in this way as the English language is not purely phonetic (eg. t-h-e).

In general a 'mixed' approach to reading is recommended. Some words are learned by blending the sounds of their letters and others by look-and-say, whole word or sentence methods.

This book provides the link with writing for the words in Readers 9a and 9b.